# Science PROJECTS & EXPERIMENTS

**NOTE TO PARENTS:**
**Some** of the experiments can be a bit messy! Please be sure your little scientist is well-supervised while performing the following projects and experiments. Have fun!

## Table of Contents

# Experiment #1: Growing Gummy Bear

*Explanation on page 9*

## What you need:
- Small cup of water
- Gummy bear candy
- Ruler

## Result Timing:
- Overnight

What do you think will happen when you leave a gummy bear in water overnight? Can you guess? In science, this kind of guess is called a *prediction*.

The steps we take to see if a prediction is *accurate* (correct) are called an *experiment*. *(When you do an experiment, it's important to follow the directions carefully and to watch closely to see what happens at each step.)*

Circle your prediction.

**a** The gummy bear will get BIGGER.

**b** The gummy bear will get SMALLER.

**c** The gummy bear will stay the same size.

## Directions: . . . . . . . . . . . . . . . . . . . . . . . . . . .

1. First, measure the length and width of your gummy bear:

| length:<br>(top to bottom) | 1 inch | width:<br>(side to side) | 1 inch |
|---|---|---|---|

2. Draw an outline of your gummy bear in the **Before** box.
3. Put the gummy bear in the cup.
4. Fill the cup with enough water to cover up the gummy bear.
5. Let the gummy bear soak in the water overnight.
6. Check the gummy bear in the morning.
7. Draw an outline of your gummy bear after the experiment in the **After** box.2

Before:

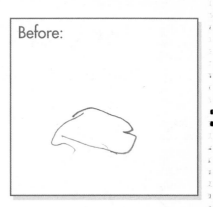

After:

# Experiment #2: String of Spikes

*Explanation on page 9*

Osmosis strikes again! If you did the "Growing Gummy Bear" experiment, you know that osmosis is the way that water tends to move from "wetter" places into "drier" places. Now we'll see what happens when the water being moved by osmosis isn't just plain water but has something else *dissolved* in it (mixed into it).

## What you need:
- 12 inches of cotton string
- Baking soda
- 2 plastic cups
- Water
- Tablespoon

## Result Timing:
- 2 days

## Directions:
1. Fill the plastic cups with water.
2. Add 1 tablespoon of baking soda into each cup.
3. Put one end of the string in one cup and the other end of the string in the other cup.
4. Let the string and the cups sit for two days. *(Do not stir, shake, jiggle, wiggle, or do anything else to the cups while you're waiting!)*
5. After 2 days, check on the experiment. What do you see? Draw a picture of what the string looked like before the experiment and after the experiment.

| Before: | After: |
|---|---|
| | |

# Experiment #3: Colorizing Plants
*Explanation on page 9*

What do plants need in order to grow and be healthy? Put a check mark next to each correct answer:

- ☐ Sunlight
- ☐ Air
- ☐ Water
- ☐ The right temperature
- ☐ Soil
- ☐ Cupcakes
- ☐ Room to grow

Okay, cupcakes were just on the list to see if you were reading carefully, but the rest are all correct answers! Have you ever wondered how plants pull water out of the soil with their roots and send it up into the rest of the plant? Try this and you'll see how it works!

## What you need:
- Tall clear glass *(or vase)*
- Water
- Red or blue food coloring *(Use liquid food coloring, not the gel kind.)*
- Long piece of celery with the leaves still attached

## Result Timing:
- Overnight

## Directions:
1. Color the celery how it looks before you start the experiment.
2. Fill the tall glass with water.
3. Add a few drops of red or blue food coloring to the water.
4. Put the celery in the water and leave it there overnight.
5. In the morning, take a look at the celery. What's different about the celery after being in colored water all night? Color how the celery looks now.

Before:

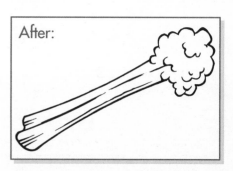

After:

# Experiment #4: Freeze and Frost

*Explanation on page 9*

Frost is the thin layer of ice that forms on grass, trees, cars, and other things when the weather turns cold. Why do you think this happens?

|  |
|---|
|  |
|  |

Let's make some frost *inside* the house so we can see how it really works.

## What you need:
- Metal coffee can with plastic lid *(empty, clean and dry, **or** a small stainless steel mixing bowl, plastic wrap and a rubber band)*
- 8–10 ice cubes
- ½ cup of salt
- Spoon

## Result Timing:
- 30 minutes

## Directions:
1. Put the ice cubes in the coffee can.
2. Pour the salt on top of the ice cubes and then use the spoon to stir the salt and ice a few times.
3. Put a lid on top of the container, or cover it tightly with plastic wrap and rubber band.
4. Let the can sit on a table or counter. Check back in 10 minutes and again at 20 and 30 minutes—do you see anything happening on the outside of the container?

| Time: | What I see: |
|---|---|
| 10 minutes |  |
| 20 minutes |  |
| 30 minutes |  |

# Experiment #5: Invisible Skin
*Explanation on page 10*

Did you ever wonder how polar bears are able to survive swimming in the freezing cold waters of the Arctic? It's because of this simple fact: *Water and oil don't mix.*

## What you need:
- 4–6 drops of vegetable oil
- Water faucet
- Liquid or bar soap for hand washing

## Result Timing:
- 10 minutes

## Directions:

1. Holding your hands over a sink, put about 4–6 drops of oil into one hand and then rub your hands together.

2. Turn the cold water on and let the water run over your hands. What happens when the water touches the coating of oil on your hands?

On the illustration, draw how the water looks on your hands.

3. Rub some soap into your hands and put them back in the water. What happens when the water touches your clean hands?

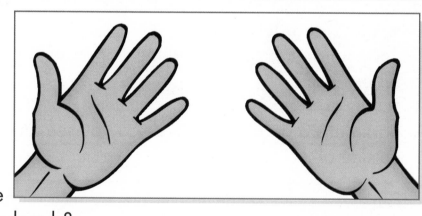

# Experiment #6: Super Soapy Boat
*Explanation on page 10*

This is a neat trick to show your friends! With an index card, you can make a boat that will ZOOM across the water—and all you have to do to make it go is to squeeze in a drop or two of liquid dish detergent.

## What you need:
- Index card
  *(or a 3x5-inch piece of manila file folder or cardstock)*
- Scissors
- Sink
  *(or a large rectangular baking dish)*
- Water
- Liquid dish detergent

## Result Timing:
- 1 minute

## Directions:
1. Draw the outline of a rowboat on the index card *(pointed at one narrow end, squared off at the other end)*. Add a small square notch in the center of the square end. *See picture.*
2. The sink you're using for the "lake" must be clean before you start, with no leftover dirt or soap in it. Fill it half-full of water.
3. Place the boat gently on top of the water at one end of the sink.
4. Squeeze a few drops of the dish detergent into the space where you cut the notch out of the end of the boat. What happens?

# WATER, WATER EVERYWHERE!

Look up, down, forward, backward
and diagonally to find these words.

prediction

water

osmosis

displace

buoyancy

observations

capillary action

condensation

evaporation

water vapor

molecule

dissolve

salt

surface tension

S N S I S O M S O C
U O R C M C R C M A
R I G F W O G S W P
F T B B A N B N A I
A A D U T D D O T L
C R I O E E I I E L
E O S Y R N S T R A
T P S A V S P A V R
E A O N L A L V A Y
N V L C I T A R P A
S E V Y E I C E O C
I A E T A O E S R T
O N W P L N Q B M I
N E L U C E L O M O
P R E D I C T I O N

ANSWERS ON PAGE 32

# Water Experiment Explanations!

**#1 Growing Gummy:** The gummy bear grows bigger because it soaks up water. This process is called *osmosis*. Water naturally moves from areas that have a high water content to areas nearby that have less water. Osmosis tries to balance "wetter" areas with "drier" ones, so that there isn't as much of a difference in the water content between the two areas. A gummy bear contains very little water. When you put it into a bowl of water, the "dry" gummy bear attracts water and grows as it holds more and more water.

**#2 String of Spikes:** The water is attracted to the string because the string is drier than the water. It brings the baking soda with it, gradually soaking higher up the string. The baking soda collects on the string and forms small clumps or spikes.

**#3 Colorizing Plants:** When a plant's roots grab onto water from the soil—or, like our celery, from water they're standing in—the narrow tubes in the plant's stem (kind of like drinking straws) carry the water upward to the other parts of the plant. This is called *capillary action* (a *capillary* is a very narrow tube). Since water molecules stick together, each tiny bit of water that enters the tubes at the bottom of the plant pulls up more water molecules with it.

*So that's why...* Another way to see *capillary action* is to hold up a paper towel while dipping one corner of it into a small puddle of water. What happens? The water climbs up into the dry parts of the paper towel. The water molecules are "sticky" and tend to stay together, so more and more water is pulled into the paper towel, spreading even into the areas that didn't touch the puddle.

*Try this:* Do the colored water experiment using a white carnation or daisy. Write down your prediction first and then compare it to what actually happens.

**#4 Freeze and Frost:** You should see frost forming on the outside of the container, starting at the bottom, within 10–20 minutes. Hmmm…. If the ice cubes are on the *inside* of the container, why did frost (ice) form on the *outside* of the container?

It's because of a process called *condensation*. Even when there's not a cloud in the sky, there is water we can't see—*water vapor*—in the air around us. As the temperature cools, some of that invisible water vapor changes into liquid water that we can see and touch. In our experiment, the ice causes the sides of the container to become much cooler than the air around the container. This cooling caused the water vapor to change into liquid water where it touched the container and then to freeze, forming a coating of frost.

*So that's why...* Have you noticed how the outside of a glass sometimes feels wet after you pour a very cold drink into it? It's not because the drink is leaking through the glass! Instead, since the drink makes the glass cooler than the air around it, some of the water vapor in the air condenses, turning into liquid water on the outside of the glass.

**#5 Invisible Skin:** Water is made of extremely tiny pieces called *molecules*. The molecules of water stick together very tightly. The molecules that make up oil are arranged differently from water molecules, so when they're put together, the oil molecules won't easily *dissolve* into (mix into) the water. You probably noticed that the water rolled off your oily hands (the oil being the "invisible skin") rather than washing the oil off with it—the water molecules stick to other water molecules rather than grabbing onto the oil molecules.

*So that's why…* Now you know why polar bears don't mind swimming in freezing water. Their fur is very oily and so it acts as a kind of waterproof coat to keep the water away from their skin.

**#6 Super Soapy Boat:** At first the boat sits on top of the water without moving. The tiny molecules that make up the water stick together very tightly, so they form a kind of "invisible skin" on the top of the water which holds the boat in place. This "invisible skin" is called *surface tension*. When you add the dish detergent, the detergent breaks up the surface tension and the boat zooms ahead.

# Experiment #7: Do-It-Yourself Blue Goo

*Explanation on page 19*

Cornstarch is a white powder made from—you guessed it—corn. In cooking, the usual job of cornstarch is to make a liquid mixture thicker, so cornstarch is a common ingredient in recipes for sauces, puddings, and gravies.

What do you predict will happen if cornstarch is mixed with water?

**Your Prediction:**

Let's find out if you're right!
Roll up your sleeves and get ready to do some **squishing!**

**What you need:**
- 1 cup of cornstarch
- ½ cup of water
- Blue food coloring
  *(Liquid food coloring, not the gel kind)*
- Mixing bowl

**Result Timing:**
- 5 minutes

**Directions:**
1. Pour one cup of cornstarch into the bowl.
2. Slowly pour ½ cup of water into the bowl.
3. Add a few drops of blue food coloring to the mixture.
4. Use your hands to squish the water and cornstarch together. Don't be tempted to be neat and use a spoon—this experiment works best if you get your hands into it!

# Experiment #8: Magic Balloon

*Explanation on page 19*

With this "magic mixture" you can inflate a balloon without having to blow air into it! *This experiment can be a little messy, so set it up near the kitchen sink and have some paper towels handy for cleaning up.*

## What you need:

- Small water or juice bottle, empty and rinsed out *(The top should be small enough that you can stretch the opening of a balloon over it.)*
- Latex balloon (new)
- 4 tablespoons vinegar
- 2 tablespoons baking soda
  *Optional: a small funnel is helpful for getting the baking soda into the balloon.*

## Result Timing:

- 5 minutes

## Directions: ·····················

1. Pour the vinegar into the bottle.
2. Using a small funnel, or a piece of paper shaped into a cone, spoon the baking soda into the balloon.
3. Holding the balloon so that the baking soda doesn't tip into the bottle, stretch the opening of the balloon to fit over the neck of the bottle.
4. Slowly straighten out the balloon and tip it upside down so that the baking soda falls into the vinegar in the bottle. What happens?
5. Draw pictures of the balloon and bottle as they looked before the experiment and after the experiment.

Before:

After:

# Experiment #9: Emerald City Pennies
*Explanation on page 19*

Do you know the story of *The Wonderful Wizard of Oz*? When Dorothy, the Scarecrow, the Tin Man, and the Cowardly Lion arrive in the wizard's Emerald City, they find that everything's green: the houses, the streets, the clothing the people wear—even the pennies are green! You can make real pennies turn green and you don't need to borrow Dorothy's green eyeglasses to do it. All it takes is a little vinegar and a little patience.

## What you need:
- Paper towel
- 2 clean, shiny pennies
- Vinegar *(about ¼ cup)*
- Small bowl

## Result Timing:
- Overnight

## Directions:
1. Draw a picture of the pennies. What color crayons or markers come closest to the color of the real coins? _____
2. Fold the paper towel in half, and then fold it in half again into a square.
3. Put the folded paper towel in the bottom of the bowl.
4. Slowly pour vinegar into the bowl until the paper towel is completely soaked. *There shouldn't be a puddle of extra vinegar sitting on top of the paper towel.*
5. Put the pennies on top of the wet paper towel and leave them there overnight.
6. The next day, take the pennies out of the bowl. How did they change? Did they change on both sides or only one side?
7. Draw a picture of the pennies the way they look now. What color crayons or markers do you need this time? _____

Pennies before:

Pennies the day after:

# Experiment #10: Crashing Colors
### *Explanation on page 20*

I bet you already know that some colors—red, blue, and yellow—are called *primary* colors. (Primary means "first" or "most important.") These colors can be *combined* (mixed together) to make other colors. Do you know what colors you can make with these pairs of primary colors?

| Primary Color Mixtures: | Your Prediction: |
|---|---|
| 1. Blue + Yellow makes: | |
| 2. Red + Blue makes: | |
| 3. Yellow + Red makes: | |

Here are the answers, but I'm afraid some of the letters crashed into each other and now they're all mixed up. Can you unscramble them?

| Primary Color Mixtures: | Unscramble: | Your Answer: |
|---|---|---|
| 1. Blue + Yellow makes: | E N G E R | Green |
| 2. Red + Blue makes: | L R U P P E | Purple |
| 3. Yellow + Red makes: | G N E R O A | Orange |

In this experiment we'll see what happens when three primary colors "bump" into each other. But here's the thing to remember—don't stir! We're not going to mix the colors; we're going to let a little detergent do that job for us.

## What you need:

- Cereal bowl
- Skim milk
- Red, blue, and yellow liquid food color *(Gel food coloring won't work in this experiment.)*
- 1 tablespoon of liquid dish detergent

## Result Timing:

- 5 minutes

## Directions:

1. Fill the cereal bowl with skim milk *(not quite to the top)*.
2. Gently add a few drops of red color into the milk in a small spot at the edge of the dish. Repeat with blue and yellow, moving around the dish's edge so that each color is as far from the other two colors as you can make it. *Do not stir the milk or jiggle the bowl!*
3. Slowly pour a little detergent into the middle of the bowl. Draw and color what you see!

Draw or describe what you see.

# Experiment #11: Groovy Lava Lamp

*Explanation on page 20*

*Explanation on page 20*

Mix It Up! / Mixture Experiments

Have you ever seen a Lava® Lamp? Large, colorful blobs of liquid float from one side to the other as the lamp container is warmed by a light bulb or tilted back and forth. Lava Lamps are fun to watch! They're also a demonstration of how inventors can use a science fact—such as "water and oil don't mix"—to create something new.

You can make your own lamp container *(without the light bulb)* to see how those blobs of "lava" stay together.

## What you need:
- Empty 2-liter plastic soda bottle *(washed and rinsed, with cap)*
- Large bottle of vegetable oil
- Water
- Food coloring *(liquid)*
- Plastic cup
- Spoon
- Funnel *(Optional—helpful for pouring things into the soda bottle without spilling.)*

## Result Timing:
- 10 minutes, overnight

## Directions: · · · · · · · · · · · · · · · · · · · · · · · · · · · · · · · · ·
1. Fill a plastic cup with water.
2. Add a few drops of food coloring to the water and stir to mix it.
3. Pour vegetable oil into the empty bottle until it is ½ full.
4. Add the colored water to the soda bottle.
5. Put the cap on the soda bottle. Ask a grown-up to make sure the cap is on tight! *Don't stir or shake the bottle, at least not yet.*

6. Gently turn the bottle sideways.
7. Draw and color what the water and oil look like now.

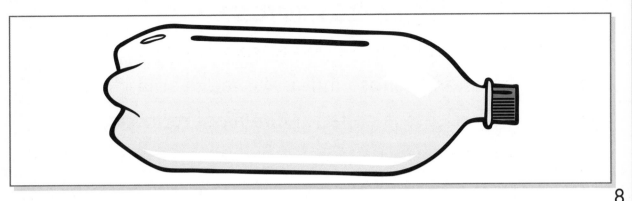

8.

Try the variations in the chart. Draw and color your observations.

| Try this: | Your Observations: |
|---|---|
| With the bottle on its side, tilt it gently back and forth. What happens to the water and oil? | |
| Shake the bottle up and down to try and mix the water and oil. What do you see now? | |
| Let the bottle stand on the counter overnight. What do you notice in the morning? | |
| Now that the contents have "settled" overnight, turn the bottle on its side again and gently tilt it back and forth. What do you see? | |

# WORD REACTION!

When we mix things together and something happens to change those things, or make something new, the process is called a *chemical reaction*.

See how many words you can make from the letters in:

# CHEMICAL REACTION

_____    _____

_____    _____

_____    _____

_____    _____

_____    _____

_____    _____

_____    _____

_____    _____

_____    _____

_____    _____

ANSWERS ON PAGE 32

# Mixture Experiment Explanations!

**#7 Do-It-Yourself Blue Goo:** The particles of cornstarch are too large to dissolve (break apart and disappear) in the water. Instead, as you mix the cornstarch with the water, slimy strings of goo form! The goo is an example of a *colloid*, a special kind of mixture in which *particles* (tiny pieces) of one type of material are *suspended* (floating) in another kind of material. The particles are so small that you may not be able to see that they are actually separate from the liquid or gas in which they are floating unless you can look at the mixture under a *microscope*.

Make sure that you tell your parents that the experiment was about making a colloid—that sounds a lot more scientific than telling them you made blue goo!

**More colloid mixtures:**
Fog = water particles floating in air
Milk = particles of milk fat suspended in a watery liquid
Jello™ = particles of gelatin and sweetener suspended in water
Oil paint = particles of *pigment* (color) floating in an oily liquid
Mayonnaise = oil suspended in water, with the help of egg yolks to keep the oil and water from separating, and flavorings to make the mixture taste good on a sandwich!

**#8 Magic Balloon:** When you mix substances like vinegar and baking soda, you cause a *chemical reaction*. The chemical reaction changes the original ingredients in some way. In this case, vinegar and baking soda "react" to each other and produce *carbon dioxide*. Although carbon dioxide is an invisible gas, we can "spot" it in two stages of this experiment: First, when the baking soda is dumped into the vinegar, carbon dioxide is produced and it makes the vinegar bubble. Second, the carbon dioxide rises through the vinegar into the air where it's caught in the balloon. The reaction should produce enough carbon dioxide to at least partially blow up the balloon.

*So that's why...* Have you ever wondered why there are all those tickly little bubbles in soda? Carbon dioxide is squashed into the soda can along with the flavored drink. This process is called *carbonation*.

**#9 Emerald City Pennies:** The main ingredient in pennies is a metal called *copper*. It's copper that gives pennies their reddish-brown color.
Vinegar contains a chemical called *acetic acid*. When acetic acid touches copper, something new is created—a green-blue chemical called *carbon acetate*. In science, we call this kind of change a *chemical reaction*. The chemicals in the vinegar and in the copper react (change) when they are combined, making carbon acetate on the pennies.

Did you notice that the tops of the pennies changed color, but not the bottoms? That's because this chemical reaction can only happen if something else is available—*oxygen* from the air around us. The tops of the pennies are exposed to the air and so oxygen is available to be part of the chemical reaction. The bottoms of the pennies don't change because they don't have enough oxygen next to them to make the reaction possible.

**#10 Crashing Colors:** Just like water, milk is made of *molecules*, tiny pieces that stick together. They stick so closely that when you put in food coloring, the food coloring (for the most part) just sits on top of the milk. Scientists call this "trick" *surface tension*—the molecules stick together as if there is an invisible skin across the top of the milk. When you add detergent to the milk, it pulls the milk molecules apart so that surface tension is weakened. The milk and detergent molecules move around, and so does the food coloring! Where the colors mix, you may see a little green, orange, or purple.

**#11 Groovy Lava Lamp:** The science fact we're working with here is that "oil and water don't mix." Their *molecules*, the small particles they're made of, don't fit together well enough for them to stay mixed together, even when you shake the bottle up and down. The oil blobs become much smaller when you shake the bottle, but when you stop shaking the bottle and let it stand still for a while, the oil bubbles start moving back together to form bigger "blobs" again.

Left on the counter overnight, the oil and water will have time to separate almost completely. You'll see that the colored water sinks to the bottom, and the oil forms a layer on top of it. The oil rises to the top because it is less *dense* than the water. *Density* is how much an object weighs compared to the *volume* of the space it takes up. In other words, if you have the same volume of water and oil—let's say one cup of each—the water weighs more than the same amount of oil.

Notes:

# Experiment #12: Clicking Quarter

*Explanation on page 30*

In this experiment, we're going to give you a little bit of the explanation first: When air gets warmer, it *expands* (grows bigger) to fill more space.

> What happens when air gets cooler? Circle your prediction.
>
> **a** It takes up less space.
>
> **b** It takes up more space.
>
> **c** It doesn't change at all.

## What you need:
- Quarter
- Freezer
- Water
- 2-liter plastic soda bottle

## Result Timing:
- 12 minutes

## Directions:
1. Take the cap off the soda bottle and put the empty bottle in the freezer for 10 minutes.
2. After 10 minutes, wet the quarter with water.
3. Take the bottle out of the freezer and set it on a table or counter.
4. Immediately cover the opening of the bottle with the quarter.

> What do you see?

> What do you hear?

# Experiment #13: Bending Light
## *Explanation on page 30*

You don't need the strength of a superhero to make light bend... it happens all the time!

### What you need:
- Glass or clear cup
- Water
- Pencil

### Result Timing:
- 1 minute

**Directions:** . . . . . . . . . . . . . . . . . . . . .
1. Fill the glass ¾ full with water.
2. Put the pencil in the glass. Hold the pencil straight up and down.
3. Look through the side of the glass. Draw a picture of the pencil.
4. Let the pencil lean against the side of the glass on a slant.
5. Look through the side of the glass. Does the pencil look different from before? Draw a picture of what the pencil looks like now.

Draw the pencil held straight in the glass.

Draw the pencil leaning in the glass.

# Experiment #14: Water Magnifying Glass
*Explanation on page 30*

Do you know what a *magnifying glass* is? A magnifying glass uses a curved piece of glass called a *lens* to make things look larger than they are. A magnifying glass works because light bends when it moves from the air through the glass lens. What is it called when light bends like this? _____

*(Hint: Read the explanation for Experiment #13 "Bending Light".)*

---

Unscramble the letters to see if you are right.

**I O R R N E F C A T** _____

---

Let's make our own "magnifying glass" using water as the lens.

## What you need:
- Small clear plastic bag
  *(a sandwich bag works well)*
- Water
- Page of writing
  *(from a newspaper or magazine)*

## Result Timing:
- 1 minute

## Directions:
1. Write some of the words from the newspaper or magazine page. Be sure to make them the size you see.
2. Pour a spoonful of water into the corner of the plastic bag.
3. Carefully hold the water-filled corner of the plastic bag over the piece of newspaper text. Look through the water at the words on the page. Write the words the size they appear when you view them through the water.

| Write the words with no lens. | Write the words as they appear through the water lens. |
|---|---|
|  |  |

# Experiment #15: Do-It-Yourself Rainbow

*Explanation on page 30*

Can you name all 7 of the colors found in a rainbow?

*(For a hint, the first letter of each color is provided.)*

R_ _  O_ _ _ _ _ _  Y_ _ _ _ _

G_ _ _ _ _  B_ _ _  I_ _ _ _ _ _  V_ _ _ _ _

**You** can make a little rainbow right in your house! This rainbow won't have a pot of gold at the end of it, but it's still a pretty cool trick. To be honest, even real rainbows you see in the sky don't have a pot of gold at the end of them—but they are beautiful to see, aren't they?

## What you need:
- Water
- Large clear drinking glass
- Small mirror
- Flashlight
- Room with white walls

## Result Timing:
- 5 minutes

## Directions:
1. Fill the glass about ⅔ full of water.
2. Submerge the mirror in the glass and tilt the mirror so it faces slightly upward.
3. Take the glass and mirror into a dark room with white or light-colored walls.
4. Shine the flashlight on the mirror.
5. Look around you—do you see a little rainbow on one of the walls? If not, try tilting the mirror and moving the flashlight until you can see a rainbow. It won't be as big and dramatic as the rainbows we see outdoors, but you should be able to notice the rainbow colors as narrow stripes.

# Experiment #16: Silly Spinning Contest

*Explanation on page 30*

If we put two balls in a bowl of water, and one ball is fuzzy and the other is smooth, will one of them spin faster than the other?

Circle your prediction.

**a** The smooth ball will spin faster than the tennis ball.

**b** The fuzzy tennis ball will spin faster than the smooth ball.

**c** Both balls will spin about the same.

## What you need:
- Bowl of water
- Smooth rubber or plastic ball
- Tennis ball

## Result Timing:
- 5 minutes

## Directions:
1. Put the smooth rubber or plastic ball into the water. Give it a spin. Does it spin a lot or just a little? Write in your answer.
2. Put the tennis ball in the water and give it a spin. Record your observation.

Smooth ball:

Fuzzy ball:

### Which ball spins faster?
*(If you're not sure, try spinning both balls at the same time.)*

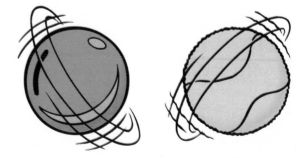

# Experiment #17: Polka Dots and Color Blots

*Explanation on page 31*

Try this experiment and you'll see that some-times a color isn't exactly what it seems.

## What you need:

- White paper coffee filter *(or thick paper towel)*
- Water-based markers in various colors including black

  *(Permanent markers won't work for this!)*
- Cup of water

## Result Timing:

- 10 minutes

## Directions: . . . . . . . . . . . . . . . . . . . . . . . . . . . . . . . . . . . . . . . . . . . .

1. Work on a table (or the floor) where a little bit of a mess won't be hard to clean up.
2. Lay the coffee filter (or paper towel) down flat on your work surface.

   *(Use the flat circle that is the bottom of the filter.)*
3. Use the markers to make dots of color in several spots on the paper towel or filter. Leave an inch or more of empty space between your dots.
4. Put your finger in the cup of water, and then let a drop or two of water fall onto each of the colored dots on the filter. Record what happens.

   *(You'll see the results even more clearly after the filter dries for a few minutes.)*

Draw or describe your observation:

# Experiment #18: Magic Money
*Explanation on page 31*

Do your parents ever tell you that "money doesn't grow on trees"? That's the kind of thing parents say when they want you to realize that money is something that has to be earned before it can be spent; and earning money can be hard work.

On the other hand, making "magic money" is easy. Here's a fun trick to show your parents. Ask them for two quarters and tell them you'll turn those two quarters into three! *(This experiment works just as well with two pennies, two nickels, or two dimes—but if you're going to ask your parents for money, wouldn't you rather get quarters than pennies?)*

**What you need:**
• 2 coins

**Result Timing:**
• 1 minute

**Directions:** . . . . . . . . . . . . . . . . . . . . . . . . . . . . . . . . . . .
1. Hold both coins in a stack between your thumb and index finger.
2. Slide the coins back and forth as fast as you can between those two fingers without letting them drop.
3. Record what you see.

Draw or describe your observation:

# Experiment #18: Pencil Perception
### Explanation on page 31

Explanation on page 31

Physics Tricks / Physics Experiments

You've probably noticed that things look a little different when you use one eye instead of both eyes. That's because your eyes work together to give you a more accurate picture of what you're seeing than you could see with just one eye.

## What you need:
- 2 sharpened pencils

## Result Timing:
- 1 minute

Will it be easier or harder to bring the two pencil points together with one eye shut? Circle your prediction.

| Your Prediction: | |
|---|---|
| EASIER | HARDER |

## Directions: . . . . . . . . . . . . . . . . . . . . . . . . . . . . . . . . . . . . .

1. Put one pencil in each hand and hold them about 12 inches in front of you.
2. Close one eye.
3. Bring the pencils together so that the points are touching.
4. Now with both eyes open, repeat step three.

Is it easier or harder to match the pencil points with both eyes open than with one eye closed? _____

Why do you think that's so? _____

Try it with your left eye and your right eye. What happens?

| Left eye: | |
|---|---|
| Right eye: | |

# MATCHING PHYSICS

Draw a line from the word on the left to the
explanation on the right which matches it.

**a** density

**b** refraction

**c** magnify

**d** rainbow

**e** three-dimensional

**f** friction

**g** chromatography

**h** optical illusion

**i** depth

**j** red, orange, yellow,
green, blue, indigo,
violet

1. The seven colors of a rainbow

2. "Color writing" — the way that water
moves different colors (or substances) at
different speeds

3. The weight of an object compared to the
amount of space it fills

4. To make something appear larger than it
actually is

5. The arches of colors we see when sunlight is
refracted through water droplets in the air

6. How light bends when it moves from one
substance into another (for example, from air
to water)

7. The way that surfaces "grab" at each other
when objects are rubbed or pushed along
each other

8. A trick where you think you see something
that isn't really there

9. Your sense of how close or far away
something is

10. Having height, width, and depth

ANSWERS ON PAGE 32

**#12 Clicking Quarter Experiment:** After sitting in the freezer for 10 minutes, the air in the bottle is now much cooler than the air in the room. When you take the bottle out of the freezer, the air inside it starts to get warmer, which means it also starts to expand. Soon there's not enough room in the bottle for the air, and it starts pushing on the quarter. The quarter clicks against the soda bottle each time the air pushes it out of the way. Within a minute or two, enough air has escaped from the bottle that it no longer pushes the quarter out of the way and the clicking stops.

So if air expands when it gets warmer, what does it do when it gets cooler? If you guessed that it takes up less space, you are right!

**#13 Bending Light Experiment:** Light moves more slowly through water than it does through air. This causes light to "bend" when it moves from air into water. This is called *refraction*.

When you hold the pencil straight up and down, you may notice that the pencil looks a tiny bit crooked or bent at the top edge of the water due to refraction. (However, the difference may be so small you don't even notice it.) When you let the pencil stand at an angle against the side of the glass, the angle makes refraction more dramatic—now the pencil looks as if it's almost cut in half at the top edge of the water.

*So that's why...* Refraction explains why objects at the bottom of the pool aren't where they appear to be when you jump in to find them. Can you think of other examples of refraction?

**#14 Water Magnifying Glass Experiment:** As we saw in the "Bending Light" experiment, water slows down light and makes it bend. In this experiment, the water in the bag bends the light almost like a magnifying glass does, so the words on the paper look larger when we read them through the water.

**#15 Do-It-Yourself Rainbow:** Do you remember learning in earlier experiments that light slows down and seems to bend when it moves from air to water? That's called *refraction* and it's part of the reason why rainbows happen. After a rainstorm, light slows down and bends where it meets water droplets in the air.

The next thing to understand is that sunlight is actually made up of seven colors, the same seven colors that are in a rainbow (red, orange, yellow, green, blue, indigo, violet). Refraction through raindrops causes those colors to separate out so you can see them as the colored bands of a rainbow.

The same things are at work when you use the mirror, the glass of water, and the flashlight. When the light bounces off the mirror in the water at just the right angle or slant, you see the colors that make up the light.

**#16 Silly Spinning Contest:** Whenever two things rub together, their surfaces grab onto each other due to a force called *friction*. This "grabbing" slows down an object, at least a tiny bit, when it slides against another object. The smoother something is, the less friction there is to slow it down.

The smooth ball spins faster in the water because it has less *friction*. The tennis ball is rough and fuzzy on the outside, so there is more friction when it rubs against the water. This increase in friction means that the tennis ball can't spin as much or as fast as the smooth ball does.

*So that's why...* Smooth surfaces produce less friction than bumpy or rough surfaces. That's why it's easier to slip on an icy sidewalk when you're wearing shoes with smooth bottoms than it is when you are wearing shoes or boots with bumpy or ridged bottoms. Can you think of other examples where it's good to have *more friction* rather than less friction?

## #17 Polka Dots and Color Blots:
Some marker colors are actually made up of a combination of other colors. When you use these colors on filter paper and add water, the water moves the color with it through the paper—but not all of the colors move at the same speed. This is why a green marker may produce a ring that's blue around it. We know that blue and yellow make green, right? When we get the green color wet, the water pulls the blue part of the ink across the filter paper at a different speed than it pulls the yellow part of the ink, so we can see shades of blue and yellow as well as the green we started with.

Scientists call techniques like this one for separating mixtures *chromatography*, which means "color writing."

## #18 Magic Money:
As you rub the coins together faster and faster, you should see a third coin! The third coin is what scientists call an *optical illusion*. "Optical" means that it has to do with your eyes, and "illusion" means that what you think you see isn't really there.

We "see" things because light bounces off of them and then goes into our eyes. Your eyes take those patterns of light and send messages about them to your brain. When things move very quickly, like the coins do in this experiment, your eyes can't keep up. In this case, the pictures your eyes have of the coins overlap and you think you see a third coin.

## #19 Pencil Perception:
Each of your eyes sees objects from a slightly different angle. This is why if you close one eye and then the other, an object close to you seems to jump back and forth as you switch eyes.

When your eyes are both open, they send information about what they see to the brain, and your brain puts that information together to make a *three-dimensional* picture. Unlike a picture drawn on a sheet of paper which has only two dimensions (height and width), what you see in the world around you has a third dimension called *depth*. Depth is the sense you have of how close or far away objects are from you.

In this experiment, most people find it's harder to match the pencil points when one eye is closed. Since your brain doesn't have information from both eyes, it's harder for you to judge depth—and you may need several tries to get the pencils to line up.

# ACTIVITY ANSWERS

## Make A Splash! Activity Answer: PAGE 8

```
S  N  S  I  S  O  M  S  O  C
U  O  R  C  M  C  R  C  M  A
R  I  G  F  W  O  G  S  W  P
F  T  B  B  A  N  B  N  A  I
A  A  D  U  T  D  D  O  T  L
C  R  I  O  E  E  I  I  E  L
E  O  S  Y  R  N  S  T  R  A
T  P  S  A  V  S  P  A  V  R
E  A  O  N  L  A  L  V  A  Y
N  V  L  C  I  T  A  R  P  A
S  E  V  Y  E  I  C  E  O  C
I  A  E  T  A  O  E  S  R  T
O  N  W  P  L  N  Q  B  M  I
N  E  L  U  C  E  L  O  M  O
P  R  E  D  I  C  T  I  O  N
```

## Mix It Up!
### Activity Answers: PAGE 18

| | |
|---|---|
| care | oil |
| create | rain |
| react | to |
| him | eat |
| her | cat |
| ice | mice |
| lace | in |
| act | alert |
| no | |
| relation | Can you |
| man | find more? |
| car | |
| reach | |
| ton | |
| not | |
| meat | |

## Physics Tricks
### Activity Answers: PAGE 29

$a = 3$

$b = 6$

$c = 4$

$d = 5$

$e = 10$

$f = 7$

$g = 2$

$h = 8$

$i = 9$

$j = 1$